Writing Fun

with

Bible Friends

Anita Reith Stohs

CPH
SAINT LOUIS

To my father, Pastor Ferdinand Reith.

1 Peter 5:4

Contents

Before the Fall (Imaginary Conversation)

Life in the Garden—Genesis 2:4–25

Adam and Eve lived happily in the Garden of Eden before the fall into sin. Write what you think they told their children about what life was like in the garden before the fall.

Adam: _____

_____

_____

Eve: _____

_____

_____

Adam: _____

_____

_____

Eve: _____

_____

_____

Adam: _____

_____

_____

Eve: _____

_____

_____

Write On: Describe what you think life today would be like if there had been no fall into sin.

Safe with the Lord
(Children's Shape Book)

The Flood—Genesis 6:1–8:22

Photocopy the ark pattern below several times. Cut out the arks to make book pages. Write and illustrate a children's story about the great flood on the ark pages. Give the book a title and make a cover for it. Staple the pages together as illustrated and read the book to a young child.

Write on: Think of other shapes you can make into children's books. Remember, the shape should relate to the story.

What a Racket! (Script for a Recording)

The Tower of Babel—Genesis 11:1–9

Crash! Bang! Clunk! Imagine what it sounded like when the people of Babel started to build their tower toward heaven. Imagine how those sounds changed when God mixed up languages the people spoke. Write the script for a tape recording of the story. Include directions for sound effects.

Write On: Record your story on an audiocassette.

Special Memories (Baby Book Entry)

The Birth of Isaac—Genesis 18:1–15; 21:1–7

Pretend you are Sarah, writing in Isaac's baby book. Write Sarah's memories of the day three heavenly visitors came to announce Isaac's coming birth.

All about Baby

_____

_____

_____

_____

_____

_____

_____

_____

_____

_____

_____

_____

_____

_____

_____

_____

_____

_____

_____

_____

_____

Write On: Write baby-book pages for other Bible babies, such as Samuel, Samson, John the Baptist, or Jesus.

Wife Wanted (Personal Ad)

Isaac and Rebekah—Genesis 24:1–67

Isaac needed a wife, so Abraham's servant was sent to find one. God led the servant to Rebekah, the wife God had picked for Isaac. What if Isaac had written an advertisement in a newspaper? What would Isaac say about himself and what he wanted in a wife? Write the rest of the Isaac's personal ad, then write one for Rebekah.

Write On: Think about what God wants people to look for in a husband or wife. Make a list of characteristics you think are important in a husband or wife.

Mesopotamian Gazette
Personals

Isaac: Single male seeks wife.

_____
_____
_____
_____
_____
_____
_____
_____
_____
_____
_____
_____
_____
_____
_____

Rebekah: Single female seeks husband.

_____
_____
_____
_____
_____
_____
_____
_____
_____
_____
_____
_____
_____
_____
_____

Field Trip to Bethel (Classroom Report)

Jacob's Dream—Genesis 28:10–22

After a dream in which he heard God speak to him, Jacob took the stone he had used for a pillow and set it up as a pillar. He named that place Bethel.

Pretend that your synagogue class (like a Sunday school class in Jesus' time) has just gone to Bethel for a field trip. Write a report on what you learned about the significance of this famous stone monument. Draw a picture to go with your report. Write a caption for the picture.

...THEN WE VISITED...

My Field Trip to Bethel

by _____

_____

_____

_____

_____

_____

_____

_____

_____

_____

_____

_____   Caption: _____

_____   _____

_____   _____

Write On: Write field trip reports for pretend visits to other historical places in the Bible.

What Do I Do Now?
(Internal Monologue)

Joseph and His Brothers—Genesis 42:1–45:15

You are Joseph, sold into slavery and now ruler over Egypt. Now, after many years, you see before you the brothers who once wanted you dead. You recognize them, but they do not recognize you. Describe your feelings.

Write On: Pretend to be one of Joseph's brothers. Write your thoughts about finding out that Joseph is alive and that he forgives you.

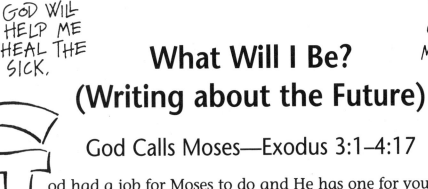

What Will I Be?
(Writing about the Future)

God Calls Moses—Exodus 3:1–4:17

God had a job for Moses to do and He has one for you too. Write what you think you will be doing in 25 years. Include ways you will be able to help do God's work at that time. Glue or tape a current picture of yourself next to your writing. Write a caption to go with the picture.

What I Will Be Doing in 25 Years

by _____

_____

_____

_____

_____

_____

_____

_____

_____

_____

_____

_____

_____

_____

_____

Caption: _____

_____

_____

Write On: Write class predictions for how different people in your class will serve the Lord when they are older.

Thank the Lord (Piggyback Song Writing)

The Songs of Moses and Miriam—Exodus 15:1–22

Moses and Miriam sang songs of joy after God led His people through the Red Sea. Think of some things you would like to thank God for.

A piggyback song is one that has new words written to a familiar tune. Write a piggyback song that thanks God for things He has done for you.

Tune: _____

Words: _____

_____

_____

_____

_____

_____

_____

_____

_____

Write On: Work with friends to come up with more piggyback songs. Sing your songs together.

My Church (Floor Plan)

Setting Up the Tabernacle—Exodus 40:1–38

od told Moses to set up a tabernacle for worship. The tabernacle was designed to be moved from place to place. What kind of church building do you worship in?

Design a new church building. First draw the floor plan for your new church, then add the outline of the furniture that will be needed. Describe the different parts of your church.

Floor Plan for a New Church

by _____

Write On: Write what will happen in the different parts of your church.

13

Which Way to Go (Notes for a Debate)

 The Spies Visit the Holy Land—Numbers 13:1–14:45

Joshua and Caleb say the children of Israel should enter Canaan. The other spies say they should return to Egypt. Prepare notes for a debate on what the Israelites should do.

On to Canaan _____

_____

_____

_____

_____

_____

_____

_____

Back to Egypt _____

_____

_____

_____

_____

_____

_____

_____

Write On: Set up a debate between the two groups of spies. Use your notes in the debate.

"I Remember Moses" (Reminiscence)

The Story of the Exodus—Exodus, Numbers, Deuteronomy

You are Caleb, the former spy, now an old man, sitting beside your grandchildren around a campfire outside your new home in the Promised Land.

"I remember Moses," you say as you begin to tell your grandchildren about your memories of this great man of God. What will you tell them about the man you followed through the wilderness for 40 years?

_____

_____

_____

_____

_____

_____

_____

_____

_____

_____

_____

_____

_____

_____

_____

Write On: Imagine your own family on the journey, following Moses from Egypt to the Promised Land. Write about your family's experience on that journey.

We Will Serve the Lord (Memo)

Joshua's Farewell—Joshua 24:1–27

"As for me and my household," Joshua said, "we will serve the LORD."

 ow can you and your family serve the Lord? Write a memo for your family, suggesting ways you can serve God together.

Write On: Write a family devotion based on the theme "We will serve the Lord." Read it to your family.

Memo for the

_____ family

_____

_____

_____

_____

_____

_____

_____

_____

_____

_____

_____

_____

_____

_____

_____

_____

_____

_____

Bible Clue (Riddle)

Samson's Riddle—Judges 14:1–20

he use of riddles at feasts and special occasions was popular during Samson's time. Pick a person from the Bible and write three or four clues about him or her. Tell your riddle to a friend, one clue at a time, and see how quickly he or she can solve it.

Sample riddle

I was the strongest judge of Israel.
I killed a lion with my bare hands.
I lost my strength when my hair was cut.
I died pushing down a temple of the Philistines.
Who am I?

Answer: Samson

Your Riddle

RIDDLE ME THIS!

GUESS WHO?

_____

_____

_____

_____

_____

_____

_____

_____

_____

_____

Write On: Write a series of riddles or clues about other Bible characters, settings, events, or objects. Take turns asking the riddles with friends or classmates.

Dear Orpah (Personal Letter)

The Story of Ruth—The Book of Ruth

You are Ruth, writing back to Moab to tell your sister-in-law, Orpah, about what happened to you and Naomi after your return to Palestine.

Write On: Write a series of letters to Orpah telling the things that happened to you and Naomi in Bethlehem.

Dear Orpah,

_____

_____

_____

_____

_____

_____

_____

_____

_____

_____

_____

_____

_____

_____

_____

_____

_____

_____

Your loving sister-in-law,
Ruth

What Happened to Hannah?
(Diary Entries)

Hannah Prays for a Child—1 Samuel 1:1–2:11

Hannah wanted a baby more than anything. Write entries in her diary to tell how God answered her prayer.

Dear Diary,
Today I was in Shiloh, at the house of the Lord . . .

_____

_____

_____

_____

_____

Dear Diary,
Today God gave me the answer to my prayers . . .

_____

_____

_____

_____

_____

Dear Diary,
Today I brought Samuel to God's house in Shiloh . . .

_____

_____

_____

_____

_____

Write On: Write diary entries to tell the stories of other people from the Bible.

Do We Need a King?
(Letter to the Editor)

Israel Asks for a King—1 Samuel 8:1–22

When Samuel grew old, the people of Israel asked God for a king. Read 1 Samuel 8:1–22 to find out why the people wanted a king and why God did not want to give them one.

Write a letter to the editor of *The Ramah Times* that expresses the opinion of one Israelite who is either for or against having a king rule the country.

IF YOU ASK FOR MY OPINION...

The Ramah Times
Letters to the Editor

Write On: Write letters to the editor about other matters debated by the children of Israel.

Praise the Lord (Haiku Poem)

Psalm 148

Psalm 148 tells the heavens and earth to praise the Lord.

Haiku poetry has three lines with a total of 17 syllables. It can also be written with 17 words. The first two lines normally tell about something in nature, and the last line makes an observation on the meaning of the first two lines.

Write a Haiku poem that praises God.

Example 1:

First line:	5 syllables	*Sparkling in the sky,*
Second line:	7 syllables	*Silvery specks wink and blink—*
Third line:	5 syllables	*Praise God for starlight.*

Example 2:

First line:	5 words	*Sparkling stars dot the sky,*
Second line:	7 words	*Winking and blinking in the dark night—*
Third line:	5 words	*Praise the Lord for starlight.*

Your Haiku

Title: _____

_____

_____

_____

_____

Write On: Write a haiku to celebrate God's creation or to paraphrase a psalm.

The King Is Dead (Obituary)

The Death of David—1 Kings 2:10

 avid, the great king of Israel, is dead. Write the obituary for him that might have appeared in a newspaper at that time. (An obituary is a notice in a newspaper that tells readers that someone has died. It gives basic information about what the person achieved in life and about his or her family members.)

Write a headline about King David. Draw a picture of the king. Write a caption for the picture.

Headline →

Caption →

The Jerusalem Journal
—— Obituaries ——

Write On: Write obituaries that tell the life story of other people from the Bible.

The Temple of the Lord
(Guidebook or Brochure)

Solomon Builds the Temple—1 Kings 6:1–38

Solomon built a great temple for worshiping God. Write a guidebook or brochure to explain the different parts of the new temple to visitors.

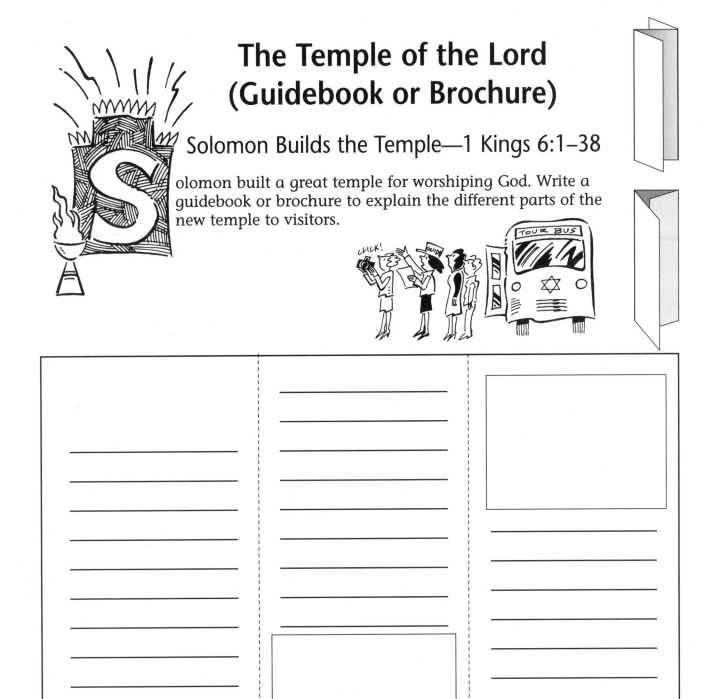

Write On: Work together with friends to write brochures for other historical sites in the Bible.

Cured at Last (Telegram)

Naaman Is Healed of Leprosy—2 Kings 5:1–27

Naaman went to Elisha to find a cure for his leprosy. After dipping himself in the Jordan River seven times, Naaman was healed.

Write a telegram for Naaman to send home to Aram to tell his wife and his servant girl of the cure God provided.

Telegram

To: My wife and servant girl

From: Naaman

_____

_____

_____

_____

_____

_____

_____

_____

_____

_____

Write On: Write telegrams to announce other dramatic events in the Bible.

24

A Super Fish Story
(Story from Another Perspective)

The Story of Jonah—The Book of Jonah

What a fish story Jonah had to tell, not about the fish that he caught, but about the one that caught him! Tell the story from the fish's point of view. Write the story inside the fish shape on this page. You can even make a fish puppet to use to tell the story to younger children.

Write On: Using the fish on this page for a pattern, copy extra pages and write a children's book for either the story of Jonah or the New Testament story of the great catch of fish (Luke 5:1–11).

The Adventures of Daniel
(Book Cover and Back Cover Copy)

Life of Daniel—The Book of Daniel

Daniel lived an exciting life. Pretend you are writing copy for the back cover of a book about Daniel. (Back cover copy is the paragraph or two on the back cover of a book. It tells you what the book is about.) Write back cover copy that will encourage people to read how God helped Daniel and his friends while they were captive in Babylon. Design the cover for the book.

Write On: Write and design book covers for other books of the Bible.

Oh, What a Beautiful Baby
(Birth Announcement)

The Birth of John the Baptist—Luke 1:57–66

The big day had come. Zechariah and Elizabeth's new baby had arrived. Write the birth announcement Elizabeth might have sent to relatives.

_____

_____

_____

_____

Write On: Include a note telling what happened when the baby was named. Or write birth announcements for other Bible babies such as Isaac or Jesus.

27

Where Christ the Savior Was Born (Annotated Map)

Jesus Is Born—Luke 1:1–2:40; Matthew 1:1–2:23

Locate Nazareth, Jerusalem, Bethlehem, and Egypt on the map. On a separate sheet of paper, write the Christmas story, breaking it down by location. For example, start with the census that took place and the journey Joseph and Mary took to Bethlehem. Add pictures, if you wish. Draw a path for Mary and Joseph to travel from Nazareth to Bethlehem.

When Jesus was a couple years old, some men from the East traveled to visit Him. They are often called the Magi or the Wise Men. Read about their journey in Matthew 2:1–12. Draw a path for their trip on the map.

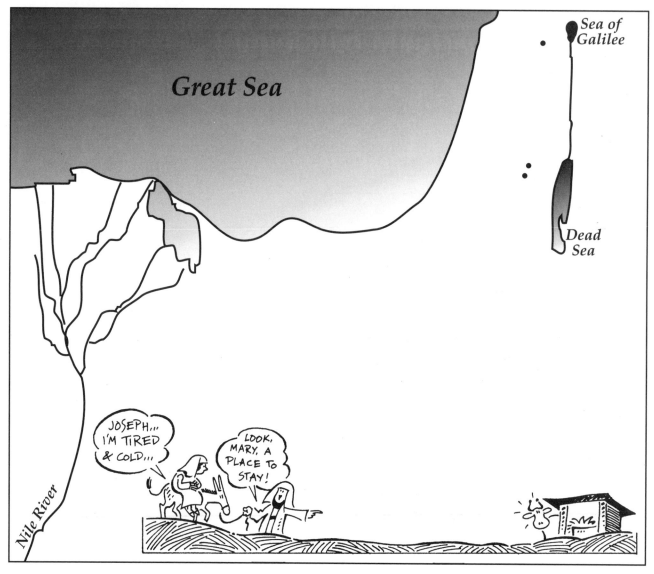

Write On: Use your map as an Advent calender. For each of the four weeks of Advent, put a star on each place identified on your map and read the part of the Christmas story written about that place. Add a star for the trip to Egypt on Epiphany Day (January 6).

28

I Have Seen Your Salvation
(Shape Prayer)

Simeon's Song—Luke 2:21–40

Simeon was filled with joy when he saw the baby Jesus. "My eyes have seen Your salvation," he prayed as he held the Christ Child in his arms.

We, too, are happy that Jesus came to save us. Inside the star write a prayer thanking God for sending Jesus, the light for all people, to be a light for your life too.

Write On: Make a prayer ornament. Trace and cut out three stars from yellow paper. Write parts of the prayer on each star. Fold each star in half. Glue the stars back to back to back to form one three-dimensional star. Punch a hole at the top, tie a ribbon through it, and hang your ornament on your Christmas tree or from the ceiling.

Talk of the Town (Speech Balloons)

The Visit of the Wise Men—Matthew 2:1–12

The coming of the Wise Men to Bethlehem must have been the talk of the town. Use speech balloons to tell what happened when the Wise Men visited. Write what these two townspeople are saying about what the Wise Men did.

Write On: Draw your own cartoon with speech balloons to tell what happened when the Wise Men avoided Herod by going home by a different route.

This Is My Beloved Son (Baptismal Card)

John Baptizes Jesus—John 1:29–34

The day Jesus was baptized by John was very special. A voice from heaven spoke and the Holy Spirit came down in the form of a dove. Make a baptismal card to give to someone you know when he or she is baptized. The picture and message will help celebrate this special day. Photocopy this page. Cut out the card and fold it in half. Design the cover of your baptismal card. Write a message on the inside of the card.

Write On: Design a baptismal banner to go with your card. Write on your banner:

"AND THIS WATER SYMBOLIZES BAPTISM THAT NOW SAVES YOU ALSO—NOT THE REMOVAL OF DIRT FROM THE BODY BUT THE PLEDGE OF A GOOD CONSCIENCE TOWARD GOD, IT SAVES YOU BY THE RESURRECTION OF JESUS CHRIST." (1 PETER 3:21)

Bible All-Stars (Collector's Cards)

The Calling of the First Disciples—Matthew 4:18–22

Simon Peter, Andrew, James, and John were the names of the first disciples Jesus called to follow Him. Use a Bible dictionary to find out more about each of these disciples. Make a collector's card for each disciple.

Write On: Make collector's cards for the rest of the disciples or for other biblical characters.

We Give Thanks (Prayer Place Mat)

Jesus Feeds the Five Thousand—John 6:1–14

Jesus took a little boy's lunch of five loaves and two fish and made it enough to feed more than 5,000 people. Before He fed the people, Jesus gave thanks for the food.

Make a prayer place mat to help you remember to thank God for the food He gives you each day.

1. In the rectangle below, write prayers for before and after meals.
2. Cut out the rectangle and glue it to a sheet of construction paper.
3. Draw or glue pictures of food around the sides of the place mat.
4. Cover (or laminate) both sides with contact paper cut 1" longer than the length and width of the construction paper.
5. Before and after meals, pray the prayers on your place mat.

Write On: Cut out several pages in the shape of a loaf of bread. Write prayers for before and after meals on the pages. Staple them together and use the prayer book with your meals.

33

Who's Walking on the Water? (Cartoon)

Jesus Walks on the Water—Matthew 14:22–33

I t's a ghost," the disciples cried one stormy night as their boat bobbed up and down on the rough waves. What happened next? Was the figure really a ghost? Draw a cartoon strip to tell the story.

Write On: Make cartoon strips to tell other Bible stories.

Clip-Clop Theater (Stick-puppet Script)

Jesus Enters Jerusalem—Matthew 21:1–11

Clip-clop, clip-clop went the little donkey's hooves.

"Hosanna! Hosanna!" the people shouted to Jesus as He rode the donkey into Jerusalem.

On a separate sheet of paper, write a puppet play that tells the story of that day. Color and cut out the characters for the story. Glue them to craft sticks. Perform the play for a group of younger children.

Write On: Make stick puppets to use in telling other Bible stories. Write scripts for those stories.

I Couldn't Believe My Eyes
(Radio Interview)

Jesus' Resurrection—Matthew 28:1–15; Luke 24:1–49

Many different people had stories to tell about Jesus' resurrection that first Easter Day: the soldiers, the two Marys, Joanna, Peter, John, the disciples on the way to Emmaus, and the disciples in the Upper Room.

Pretend you are a reporter who is interviewing one of these eyewitnesses for a radio news broadcast. Write each question and its reply. Record your interview on tape.

Person Interviewed: _____

Question: _____

Reply: _____

_____

_____

Question: _____

Reply: _____

_____

_____

Question: _____

Reply: _____

_____

Write On: Write interviews with other Bible people in both the Old and New Testaments.

36

Tongues of Fire (Poster)

Pentecost—Acts 2:1–47

he people to whom the Holy Spirit came at Pentecost spoke words of praise to God. Make a praise poster. Inside the flame shape below, use bright markers or crayons to write your own words of praise and thanksgiving to God. Cut out the flame shape and hang it up as a poster.

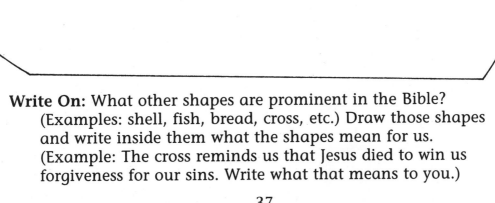

Write On: What other shapes are prominent in the Bible? (Examples: shell, fish, bread, cross, etc.) Draw those shapes and write inside them what the shapes mean for us. (Example: The cross reminds us that Jesus died to win us forgiveness for our sins. Write what that means to you.)

37

Share the Good News (Button Design)

The Early Christians—Acts 2:41–47

The early Christians shared their possessions, prayed, and praised God. They shared their Good News with others, and each day the number of believers increased.

You, too, can share your joy in Christ. Photocopy this page. Design a Good News button that could be worn as a witness to Jesus and His love. Cut out your button. Cut a cardboard circle the same size as the button. Glue the button to the cardboard. Tape a safety pin to the back of the button.

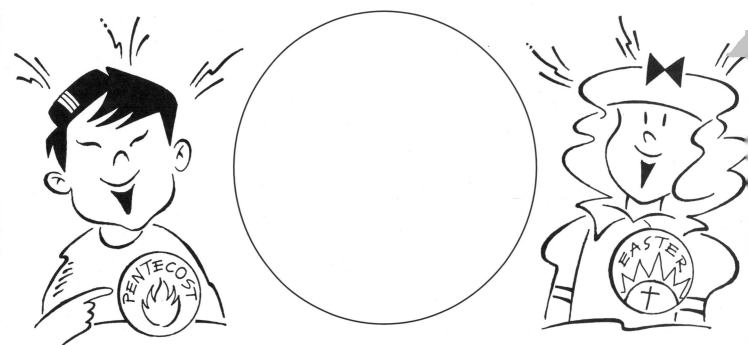

Write On: Make buttons to celebrate special seasons of the church year such as Christmas, Easter, or Pentecost.

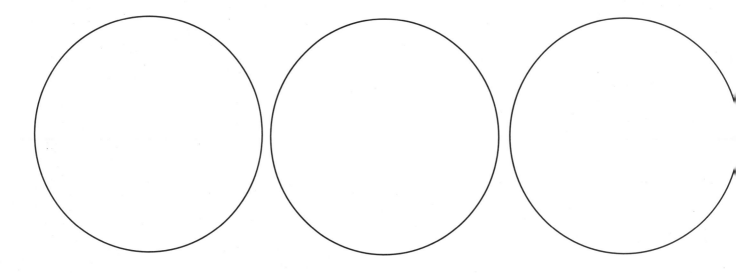

On the Road (Journal Entries)

The Conversion of Saul—Acts 9:1–25

In a flash of light, Jesus appeared to Saul and Saul changed from foe to friend. Write the diary entry Saul might have written the night before Jesus appeared to him and the entry he might have written when he could see again.

On the way to Damascus ...

_____

_____

_____

_____

_____

_____

At Damascus ...

_____

_____

_____

_____

_____

_____

_____

Write On: Use diary entries to tell more of the story of Paul after he became a missionary for Christ.

My Favorite Story (Personal Preference)

Timothy Hears God's Word—2 Timothy 1:5

Timothy heard many Bible stories from his mother and grandmother. You, too, have heard many stories about God's people in the Bible. What is your favorite Bible story? Write the story in your own words and tell why you like it and what it means to you.

_____

_____

_____

_____

_____

_____

_____

_____

_____

_____

_____

_____

Write On: Write about a favorite Bible character, parable, or psalm.

Witness on the Way (Bumper Sticker)

Philip and the Ethiopian Official—Acts 8:26–40

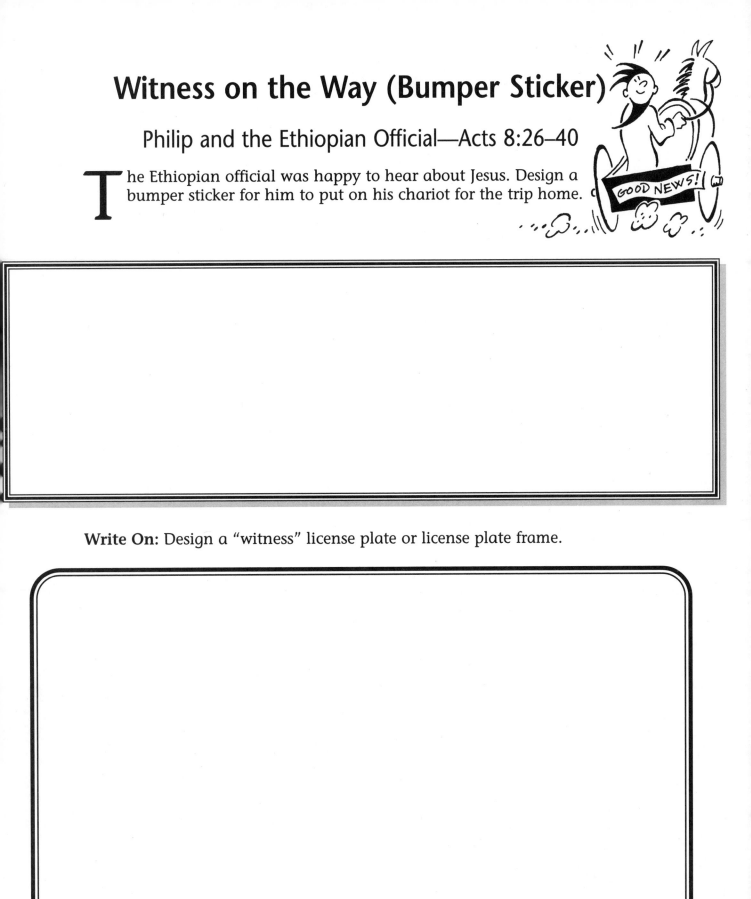

The Ethiopian official was happy to hear about Jesus. Design a bumper sticker for him to put on his chariot for the trip home.

Write On: Design a "witness" license plate or license plate frame.

Jesus' Love Is for All (Making a List)

Peter Goes to See Cornelius—Acts 10:1–48

God loved Cornelius, a Roman soldier, and wanted him to be saved. God loves all the people in our world. Inside the heart, list some of the people Jesus loves. Compare your list to a friend's list.

Write On: List ways you can help some of the people on your list learn more about God's love for them.

Earthquake! (You-Are-There News Report)

The Jailer at Philippi—Acts 16:16–40

The earth shakes and the prison collapses. You are there with your news team to record the event as it happens. Write the story as it is happening. Tape your news report in front of a video camera.

_____

_____

_____

_____

_____

_____

_____

_____

_____

_____

_____

_____

_____

_____

_____

_____

Write On: Write "on the spot" news reports about other earthshaking Bible events such as Jesus' resurrection or the parting of the Red Sea.

Lydia's Shirt Shop (T-Shirt Pattern)

Lydia's Conversion—Acts 16:11–15

ydia heard the Good News of Jesus' love for her and shared it with her family. If she lived today, perhaps she would enjoy selling T-shirts with Christian messages as a way of sharing the Good News with others. Design a Christian T-shirt for Lydia's Shirt Shop.

Write On: Design T-shirts for other Bible stories.

God's Love in Action (Magazine Article)

The Story of Dorcas—Acts 9:36–42

Dorcas made clothes for the poor. Write the feature article about her that could have been written in a church magazine at that time. Include information about how Peter raised her from the dead. Draw one or two pictures and add captions for them.

The New Christian Quarterly   **Summer Issue**

Write On: Write other articles for this issue of _The New Christian Quarterly_.

Traveling through God's Word
(Board Game)

Books of the Bible—Genesis through Revelation

List the people from the Bible about whom you have read in this book. You will need one name for each square on the game board below. Order your list so the names are chronological (the order in which the stories about them appear in the Bible). Write the names in order on the game board squares. With each name, write something about that person. (Example: **PETER**—His name means "rock.")

Genesis

GOD'S

The game instructions are started for you. Finish writing them. Decide how to pick which player goes first. Decide what happens when a player lands on a square. Play the game to see who is the first to travel through God's Word.

GAME INSTRUCTIONS:

For _____ players. Use _____ for markers.

Flip a penny to take turns. Heads = move _____ spaces; tails = move _____ spaces.

Write On: Use the game board to teach only one story or a series of stories. Or use the board to learn Bible places or passages.

WORD

Revelation

News from Malta (Postcard)

Paul's Shipwreck at Malta—Acts 27:1–28:10

What a trip—a storm and a shipwreck, followed by a snakebite. What kind of postcard do you think Paul and Luke might have written to their friends?

Dear Friends,

To: Aquila and Priscilla
Ephesus
Province of Asia

Your friends,
Luke and Paul

Write On: Use a series of postcards from Paul's missionary friends to tell a sequence of stories from one of his missionary journeys. Or describe other biblical events through postcards.